CHESTER'S MUSIC PUZZLES

By Carol
With Illustr
Wendy Hoi
Chester's Piano Books

For Patsy Anderson — Enjoy the Puzzles!

INTRODUCTION

To the Teacher

Chester's Music Puzzles can be used alongside any beginner's piano course although they are designed to match the pace of **Chester's Piano Books 1-5.** (Set 5 is written to correspond with **Chester's Piano Book Number Five,** etc).

They are for young beginners (5 years upwards) and can be used from the very first lesson. Each set is carefully graded to take into account the development of the pupils' reading and writing skills.

To start with, give your pupil the folder with just Paper 1 in it. The other papers can be handed out as the pupil progresses. Space has been left for stars — it is well worth keeping a supply to reward your pupils! There is also a certificate to be won when each set has been completed!

The information boxes are as simple as possible, to teach or remind the pupil. They are also invaluable for parents helping their children.

It is important that written work should be taught hand-in-hand with practical playing, to make the *"language"* of music much easier and more natural to learn.

To the Parent

These papers aim to give young children a real sense of enjoyment as they begin to learn the language of music. As you and your children go through each paper with Chester the Frog and his friends, learning to read and write music becomes as natural as learning to read and write words. Read through each information box with your child before trying the questions!

To the Pupil

Make sure that you use a B or a 2B pencil. Try to get a star every time! Enjoy yourselves!

Carol Barratt ♪♫

CHESTER'S MUSIC PUZZLES SET

CONTENTS

Topics

Consolidates material from Sets 1, 2, 3, and 4 plus new Major Scales (**E, A♭**), so that pupils have covered Major Scales and their Key Signatures up to 4♯s and 4♭s, Transposition, white keys having two names (i.e. **F=E♯**), new Minor Scales (**B, G, C**), so that pupils have covered **A, E, B, D, G** and **C** Minor Scales, Simple Duple and Compound Duple Time, a quick way to find the Relative Minor, finding the Relative Major, Tonic Triads (minor keys, as above), Major Scale Intervals plus Minor 2nd and Minor 3rd, Simple Triple and Simple Quadruple Time, finding the key (minor keys, **A, E, D** and **G**).

New Note and Rest Values

New Signs and Words

Andantino, Più, Sostenuto, Con, Moto, Furioso, Con Forza, Agitato, Misterioso, Doloroso, Vivace, Eleganza, Passionato
Diatonic

CHESTER'S MUSIC PUZZLES

SET

Name ....

MATCHING GAME

1. Write the correct number in the box in front of each sign.

1. Very Loud
2. Moderately Soft
3. Accent
4. Play an Octave higher

5. Pause
6. Very Soft
7. Gradually getting softer
8. Moderately Loud

Brushing up!

6.	*pp*		>
	>		*mf*
	mp		*ff*
	⌢		*8ve*

TIME SIGNATURES

2. Work out the Time Signatures for the Bars below. Then write some notes to fill each Bar.

2 ♩ beats   2 ♩. beats   3 ♩ beats

CHANGE AROUND!

3. Write out the exercise below using ♯s instead of ♭s.

CAN YOU HELP?

4. There are five dots missing below. Add the missing dots to fill each Bar.

5. The Bar Lines are missing. Can you put them in?

6. Someone has run off with the Accidentals. Can you put them back?

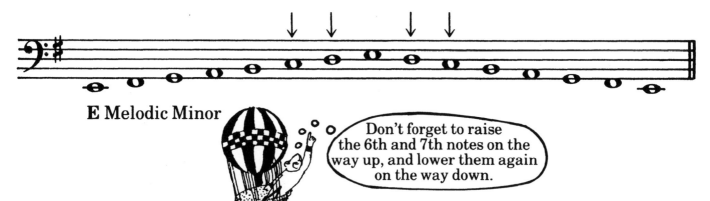

E Melodic Minor

Don't forget to raise the 6th and 7th notes on the way up, and lower them again on the way down.

MUSIC DICTIONARY

Three more Italian words for you to remember.

Andantino → Slow, but not as slow as Andante.
Più → More   Sostenuto → Sustained

7. Write out these words again in the order of Slow . . . Fast

Allegretto   Andante   Allegro   Andantino

CHESTER'S MUSIC PUZZLES

SET

PAPER 2 ☆

Name ....

NOTE WRITING

1. Write out the notes below as ♩.s using Leger Line notes.

F♯   D♭   A   E♮

E♮   D♯   F♯

NEW MAJOR SCALES

2. In the Scale below, add the ♯s needed to make the Major Scale pattern.
   Add ⌐ to the Semitones.

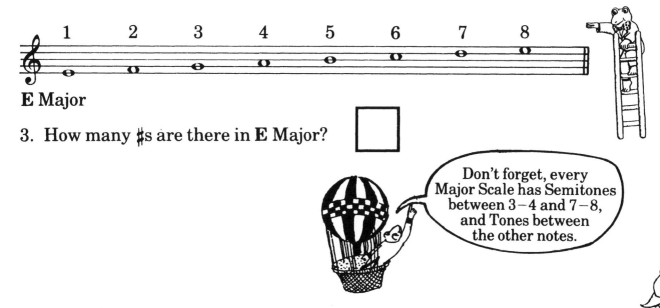

E Major

   1   2   3   4   5   6   7   8

3. How many ♯s are there in **E** Major? ☐

Don't forget, every Major Scale has Semitones between 3−4 and 7−8, and Tones between the other notes.

4. In the Scale below, add the ♭s needed to make the Major Scale pattern.
   Add ⌐ to the Semitones.

A♭ Major

5. How many ♭s are there in **A♭** Major? ☐

LET'S TRANSPOSE

Transpose → to move from one place to another.
To make sure that the Major Scale pattern stays the same when it is moved,
the Key Signature needs to be changed.

For example, the tune below is in **G** Major.
To move it down a Tone, find a
Tone lower than **G**.

The new Key will be **F** Major and the
Key Signature will be one ♭.

6. Finish transposing this tune down a Tone.

INTERVALS

7. Name these Harmonic Intervals.

8. Name these Melodic Intervals.

CHESTER'S MUSIC PUZZLES | SET

Name ....

KEY SIGNATURES – MAJOR SCALES

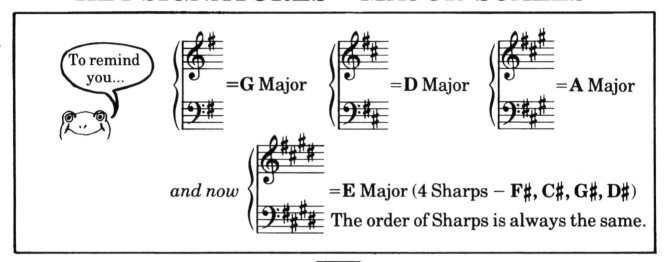

To remind you...

=G Major   =D Major   =A Major

and now   =E Major (4 Sharps – F♯, C♯, G♯, D♯)
The order of Sharps is always the same.

1. How many ♯s are there in **A** Major? ☐

   Name these ♯s in the correct order. _____

2. Write these Key Signatures.

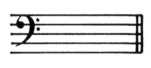

E Major

G Major

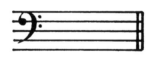

D Major

3. Write the Scale of **E** Major descending (coming down), using the Key Signature.

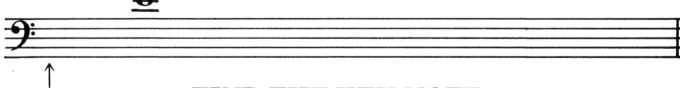

↑

FIND THE KEY-NOTE

4. Write the key-note as a ♩. , then name the Key.

G Major

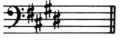

___ Major

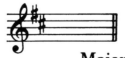

___ Major

___ Major

KEY SIGNATURES – MAJOR SCALES

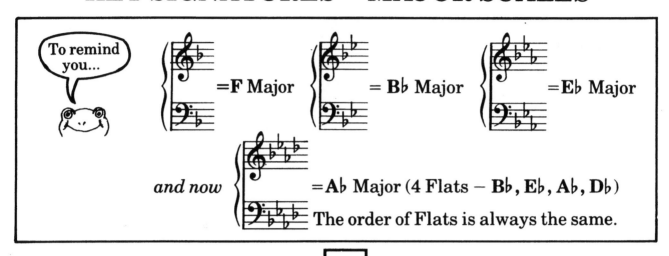

"To remind you..."

= F Major   = Bb Major   = Eb Major

and now   = Ab Major (4 Flats – Bb, Eb, Ab, Db)
The order of Flats is always the same.

5. How many ♭s are there in Eb Major? ☐

Name these ♭s in the correct order. _____

6. Write these Key Signatures.

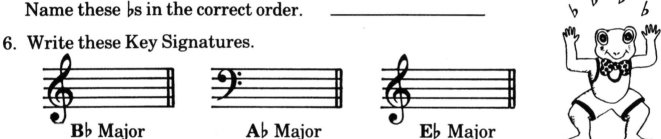

Bb Major   Ab Major   Eb Major

7. Write the Scale of Ab Major descending, using the Key Signature.

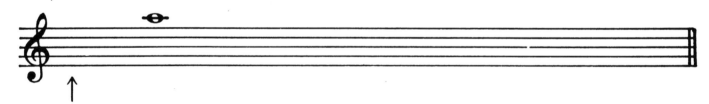

↑

FIND THE KEY-NOTE

8. Write the key-note as a ♩. , then name the Key.

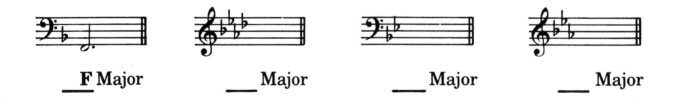

_F_ Major   ___ Major   ___ Major   ___ Major

CHESTER'S MUSIC PUZZLES | SET 5 | PAPER 4 ☆

Name ....

TRIPLETS

1. There is one beat missing in every Bar below.

   Use ♩♩♩ rhythms to fill these beats.

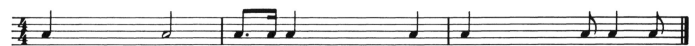

RESTING!

2. Add the missing Rests.

   Remember Rests can be dotted.

DOUBLE DOTS

A second dot after a note adds half the value of the first dot.
♩.. = ♩ ⌣ ♪ ♪   ♩.. ♪ = ♩ ⌣ ♪.♪

3. How many ♪s are there in ♩..? ☐

MUSICAL SENTENCES

4. Fill in the missing words by naming the notes.

Chester put his _____ on the train. Soon he will ____ sunning himself

at the _____ of his holiday pond.

TWO OCTAVE SCALE

5. Write the Key Signature of **G** Major and then, using ♪s grouped in 4s, write *two* Octaves of that Scale ascending.

The last **G** will be a ♩

RHYTHMS

6. Finish writing a rhythm for the words below.
   Try saying it and clapping it first.

Writ-ing mu-sic   can   be   fun   when   Ches-ter   shows   us   how   it's   done!

MORE ABOUT SHARPS AND FLATS

> In Set 4 we learned that each black key has two names →G♭ =F♯.
>
> Some *white* keys can also have two names. As **F** is a Semitone above **E**, it is sometimes called **E♯**. As **C** is a Semitone above **B**, it is sometimes called **B♯**. In the same way **E = F♭** and **B = C♭**.

7. Write each note in another way.   Then name it.

| C | B♯ | B | ___ | F | ___ | E | ___ |

SHORT RESTS!

8. Draw a Rest in each box, which has the same value as the note next to it.

CHESTER'S MUSIC PUZZLES

SET

PAPER 5
☆

Name ....

NEW MINOR SCALES

1. Look at **D** Major Scale. Circle the 6th note.

Remember
the Relative Minor
starts on this 6th note
of the Major Scale.

We are Relatives
and share a
Key Signature!

The Relative Minor of **D** Major starts on ☐

2. Write out this Relative Harmonic Minor Scale (one Octave, up and down), and then name it. Don't forget to write in the Key Signature.

⬆

_____ Harmonic Minor.

Remember Just raise the 7th note a Semitone on the way up *and* down.

3. Look at **B♭** Major Scale. Circle the 6th note.

The Relative Minor of **B♭** Major starts on ☐

4. Write out this Relative Melodic Minor Scale (one Octave, up and down), and then name it.

⬆

_____ Melodic Minor.

© Copyright for all countries 1987
J. & W. Chester/Edition Wilhelm Hansen London Ltd.

CH55845

MUSIC DICTIONARY

Con → With   Moto → Movement

Many Italian words sound like English words:
Furioso → Furiously   Con Forza → With force   Agitato → Agitated
Misterioso → Mysterious   Doloroso → Sorrowful   Vivace → Lively
Eleganza → Elegance   Passionato → Passionate

5. Write out the correct Italian words in the boxes.

With Elegance = [   ]   Lively = [   ]

THINGS TO ADD

6. Add the Time Signature.
   Add the Key Signature of **D Minor**.
   Add an Accent to the Crotchet.
   Add 2-note slurs to the Quavers and 3-note slurs to the Semiquavers.
   Show that the piece should be played Mysteriously.
   Show that the piece starts off soft and gets gradually softer.

NOTE WRITING

7. Write out the notes below as s.
   Include some Leger Line notes.

[F♯]   [D♭]   [A]

[E♯]   [C♭]   [B♯]

CHESTER'S MUSIC PUZZLES | SET | PAPER 6 ☆

Name ....

TONIC TRIADS – MAJOR KEYS

1. Look at the Key Signatures and name the Keys.
   Then write out the Tonic Triads.

   _D_ Major   ___ Major   ___ Major   ___ Major   ___ Major

2. Write out the Tonic Triads in the given Keys, *without* Key Signatures.

   D Major   **F** Major   **G** Major   **A** Major   **E** Major

CHANGE AROUND!

3. Add the Time Signature.
   Then re-write this exercise putting Rests in place of notes,
   and notes (on any line or space) in place of Rests. Make *your* ♪s Staccato.

   a)

   b)

4. Transpose 3a) above from **C** Major to **D** Major. (Up a Tone).
   Don't forget to add the Time Signature and the new Key Signature.

FINDING THE MAJOR KEY
Up to 3 ♯s and 3 ♭s

Remember look for the ♯ or ♭ which is last in the Key Signature order.
When you have found it, use it to find out the Key.

5. Name the Keys of the following phrases:

☐ Major

☐ Major

☐ Major

☐ Major

DEMISEMIQUAVERS

A Demisemiquaver looks like a Semiquaver but has three tails ♪

A ♪ is half as long as a ♪ , so ♫♫ = ♫ = ♫. = ♩

The Demisemi-spider!

𝄽 = ♪ Rest

6. How many ♪s are there in ♩.. ? ☐

7. Finish the second Bar by making Demisemiquavers in groups of eight.
    Then work out the Time Signature.

CHESTER'S MUSIC PUZZLES

SET

Name ....

A NEW MINOR SCALE

1. Look at **E♭** Major. Circle the 6th note.

The Relative Minor of **E♭** Major starts on ☐

2. Write out this Relative Harmonic Minor Scale (one Octave, up and down), and then name it.

↑

___ Harmonic Minor

> For the moment, you will not be learning any more *Minor* Scales. Make sure that you know these Minors → **A, E, B, D, G, C.** For extra practice, you could write them out in your manuscript book.

MORE ABOUT TIME

> SIMPLE TIME means the beat is an ordinary note.
> COMPOUND TIME means the beat is a dotted note.
> DUPLE means two.

TIME CHART

SIMPLE DUPLE (2 ordinary beats)	COMPOUND DUPLE (2 dotted beats)
$\frac{2}{2}$ ♩ ♩ $\frac{2}{4}$ ♩ ♩ $\frac{2}{8}$ ♪ ♪	$\frac{6}{4}$ ♩. ♩. $\frac{6}{8}$ ♩. ♩. $\frac{6}{16}$ ♪. ♪.

3. Write these Time Signatures.

Simple ══ Compound ══ Simple ══ Compound ══
Duple ══ Duple ══ Duple ══ Duple ══
2 ♩ beats ══ 2 ♩. beats ══ 2 ♩ beats ══ 2 ♩. beats ══

AT SPEED

A quicker way to find the Relative Minor of a Major, is to count *down* 3 letter-names, making sure it is 3 Semitones.	 So **D** is the Relative Minor of **F** Major.
To find the Relative Major of a Minor, count *up* 3 letter-names, making sure it is 3 Semitones.	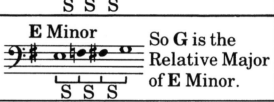 So **G** is the Relative Major of **E** Minor.

4. Write in the names of the Minor Keys related to these Major Keys.

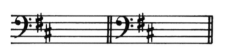  

D Major ____ Minor   **B♭** Major ____ Minor   **E♭** Major ____ Minor

5. Write in the names of the Major Keys related to these Minor Keys.

D Minor ____ Major   **E** Minor ____ Major   **G** Minor ____ Major

FLATTEN DOWN AND SHARPEN UP!

6. Keeping the same letter-name, write one Semitone *lower* than each given note. Name them both.

D   **D♭**   ____ ____   ____ ____   ____ ____

7. Keeping the same letter-name, write one Semitone *higher* than each given note. Name them both.

____ ____   ____ ____   ____ ____   ____ ____

CHESTER'S MUSIC PUZZLES — SET 5

Name ....

TREAD CAREFULLY!

1. The grouping is wrong in the exercise below.
   Re-write it, using correct Compound Duple grouping.

TONIC TRIADS – MINOR KEYS

This is a Chord made up of the Tonic, third and fifth of the *Minor* Scale.

Tonic Triad of **D** Minor →

2. Write the Tonic Triads of each Key without using the Key Signature.

  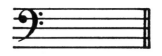 

   G Minor   E Minor   B Minor   C Minor

RHYTHMS

3. Write a rhythm in Simple Duple Time for the words below.
   Say them out loud first. Add the Time Signature.

Tongue twist-ers,	Fing-er twist-ers,	Hard work can	give you blist-ers.
>	>	>	>

ALL KINDS OF INTERVALS!

The order of Intervals in **all** Major Scales from Tonic to 5th is:

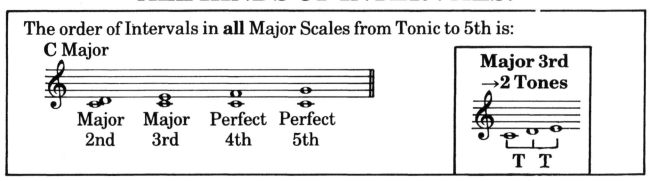

C Major

Major 2nd   Major 3rd   Perfect 4th   Perfect 5th

Major 3rd →2 Tones
T T

4. Write these Harmonic Intervals in **D Major**.

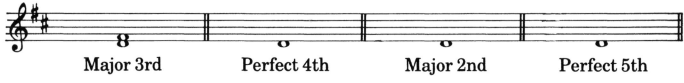

Major 3rd   Perfect 4th   Major 2nd   Perfect 5th

The order of Intervals in **all** Minor Scales from Tonic to 5th is:

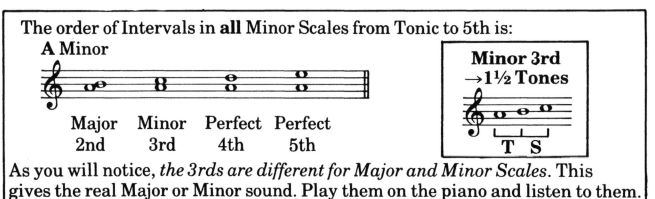

A Minor

Major 2nd   Minor 3rd   Perfect 4th   Perfect 5th

Minor 3rd →1½ Tones
T S

As you will notice, *the 3rds are different for Major and Minor Scales*. This gives the real Major or Minor sound. Play them on the piano and listen to them.

5. Write these Harmonic Intervals in **E Minor**.

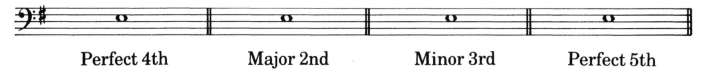

Perfect 4th   Major 2nd   Minor 3rd   Perfect 5th

6. Circle the Minor 3rds below.

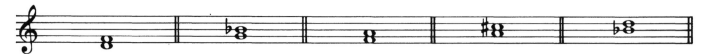

SECONDS

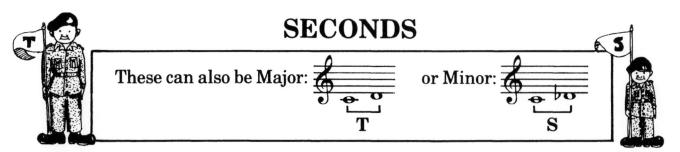

These can also be Major: or Minor:

T   S

7. Circle the Major 2nds below.

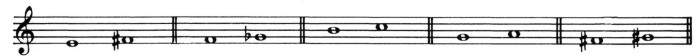

CHESTER'S MUSIC PUZZLES

SET

PAPER 9 ☆

Name ....

TIME CHART

SIMPLE TRIPLE (3 ordinary beats)	SIMPLE QUADRUPLE (4 ordinary beats)
$\frac{3}{2}$ ♩ ♩ ♩ $\frac{3}{4}$ ♩ ♩ ♩ $\frac{3}{8}$ ♪ ♪ ♪	$\frac{4}{2}$ ♩ ♩ ♩ ♩ $\frac{4}{4}$ ♩ ♩ ♩ ♩ $\frac{4}{8}$ ♪ ♪ ♪ ♪

1. Work out the Time Signatures for the Bars below.
   Then write some notes to fill each Bar.

> Watch out for the Compound Duple time!

3 ♩ beats   4 ♩ beats   2 ♩. beats

4 ♪ beats   3 ♩ beats   2 ♩. beats

SCALES TO WRITE

2. Write one Octave descending of the Major Scale with the given Key Signature.
   Use this rhythm.

$\frac{2}{4}$ ♩ ♫ | ♩ ♩ | ♩. ♪ | ♩ ‖

3. Write one Octave descending of the Harmonic Minor Scale with the given
   Key Signature.   Use this rhythm.

$\frac{3}{4}$ ♫ ♩ ♩ | ♩ ♩ ♩ | ♩. ‖

TONIC TRIADS TO WRITE

4. Write the following Tonic Triads, using Key Signatures.

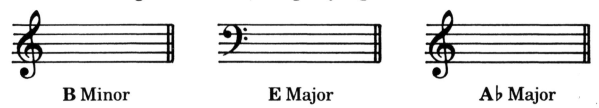

| B Minor | E Major | A♭ Major |

MORE INTERVALS

When two notes making an Interval belong to the same Key, the Interval is **Diatonic.**

SIXTHS, SEVENTHS AND EIGHTHS

In **all** Major Scales the Diatonic 6ths, 7ths and 8ths are:

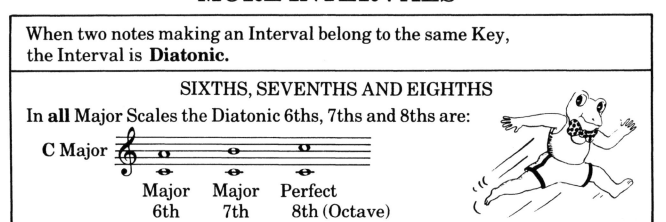

C Major

Major 6th   Major 7th   Perfect 8th (Octave)

5. Write these Harmonic Intervals.

Major 6th   Major 7th   Perfect 8th   Major 6th

RHYTHMS

6. Write a rhythm for the words below.

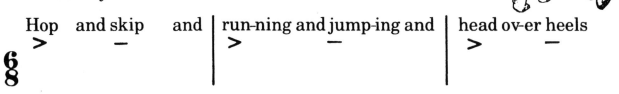

Hop   and skip   and | run–ning and jump-ing and | head ov-er heels

RESTING!

7. Add the missing Rests.

8. How many Demisemiquavers are there in the Rests below? Add them up.

2 + ___ + ___ + ___ + ___ = ☐

CHESTER'S MUSIC PUZZLES

SET

Name ....

FINDING THE KEY
(A, E, D and G MINORS)

Look for the Sharp which is last in the Key Signature order (**F♯, C♯, G♯, D♯**) → this will be the 7th note of the Scale.

Here it is **C♯**, so the key-note is a Semitone higher →**D**.

To check whether the Key is Major or Minor:

Look at the third above the key-note, and work out whether it is a Major or Minor 3rd.

Here it is a Minor 3rd, so the Key is **D** Minor. (**D** Major would have an **F♯**)

Helpful hint: if tunes contain ♯s *and* ♭s together, they are usually in the Minor Key.

1. Name the Keys of the following phrases. Help is given with a).

a)

Find the key-note and the third above:

The Interval is a: Minor 3rd

The Key is: G Minor

b)

The Key is:

_____ 3rd

_____

c)

The Key is:

_____ 3rd

_____

CHESTER TAKES SCORE!

VOLUME CONTROL		points if correct
p	=	1
ff	=	2
mf	=	2
f	=	1
mp	=	2
Your **Total** =		
		8

PLENTY OF SIGNS		
>	=	2
♮	=	1
⌒	=	1
¢	=	2
♩	=	2
Your **Total** =		
		8

WHAT SPEED?		
Presto	=	2
Allegro	=	1
Largo	=	2
Accel.	=	2
Andante	=	1
Your **Total** =		
		8

HOW TO PLAY?!		
Vivace	=	3
Con Moto	=	3
Legato	=	3
Cantabile	=	4
espr.	=	3
Your **Total** =		
		16

Your **Grand Total** = $\dfrac{\rule{1cm}{0.4pt}}{40}$

Well done! I hope you've enjoyed the Puzzles!

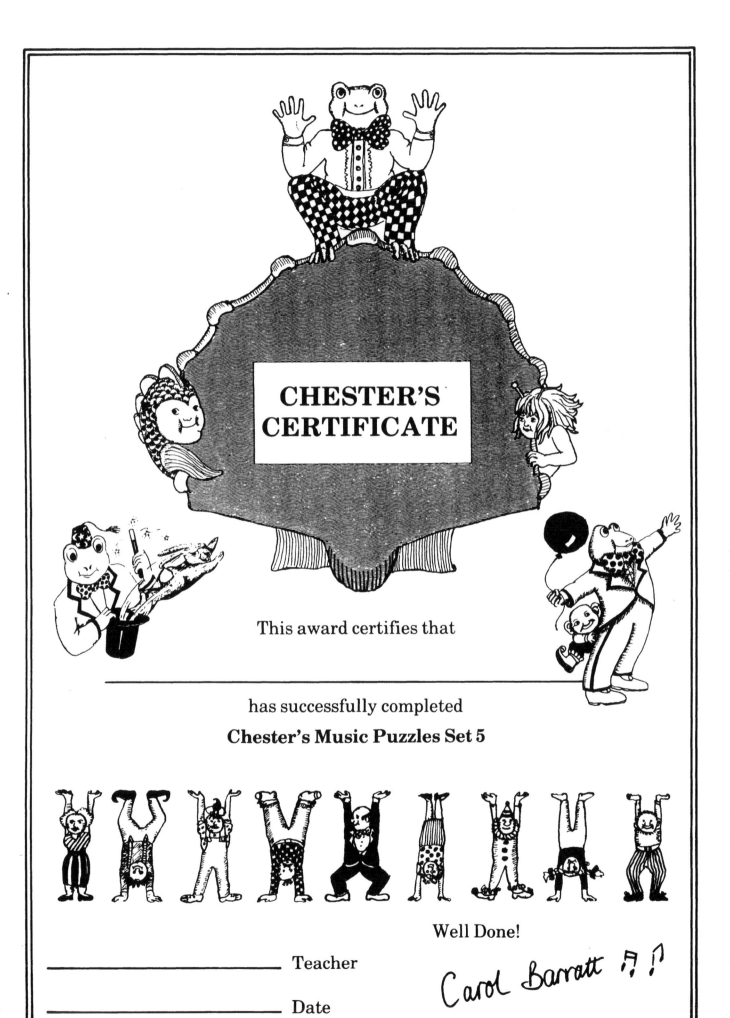

CHESTER'S CERTIFICATE

This award certifies that

_____

has successfully completed

Chester's Music Puzzles Set 5

Well Done!

_____ Teacher

_____ Date

Carol Barratt

1/09 (168607)